It's Easy To Play
All-Time Favourites

GW00686120

Classical Music

Film Themes

Jazz, Blues & Soul

Pop & Rock

Classic Hits

Showtunes

Wise Publications
part of The Music Sales Group

London / New York / Paris / Sydney / Copenhagen / Berlin / Madrid / Tokyo

Published by
Wise Publications
14-15 Berners Street, London W1T 3LJ, UK.

Exclusive Distributors:
Music Sales Limited
Distribution Centre, Newmarket Road, Bury St Edmunds, Suffolk IP33 3YB, UK.
Music Sales Pty Limited
120 Rothschild Avenue, Rosebery, NSW 2018, Australia.

Order No. AM992145
ISBN: 978-1-84772-366-6
This book © Copyright 2008 by Wise Publications.

Edited by Jessica Williams.
Compiled by Nick Crispin.
'Hung Up', 'Purple Rain', 'Sail Away and
'You're The One That I Want' arranged by Derek Jones.
Music processed by Paul Ewers Music Design.
Cover illustration by Liz Barrand.

Printed in the the EU.

Your Guarantee of Quality
As publishers, we strive to produce every book to the highest commercial standards.
The music has been freshly engraved and the book has been carefully designed to
minimise awkward page turns and to make playing from it a real pleasure.
Particular care has been given to specifying acid-free, neutral-sized paper made from
pulps which have not been elemental chlorine bleached.
This pulp is from farmed sustainable forests and was produced with special regard for the environment.
Throughout, the printing and binding have been planned to ensure a sturdy,
attractive publication which should give years of enjoyment.
If your copy fails to meet our high standards, please inform us and we will gladly replace it.

www.musicsales.com

Liebesträume

Music by Franz Liszt

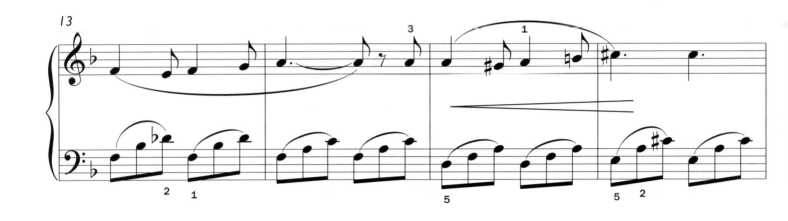

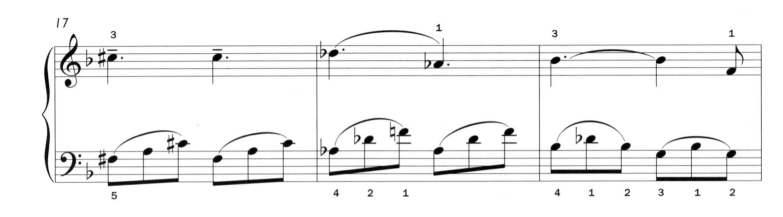

A tempo

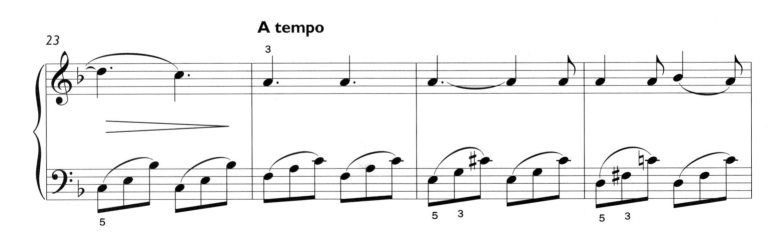

5

Clarinet Concerto
(2nd Movement: Adagio)

Music by Wolfgang Amadeus Mozart

Nimrod
(from 'The Enigma Variations')

Music by Edward Elgar

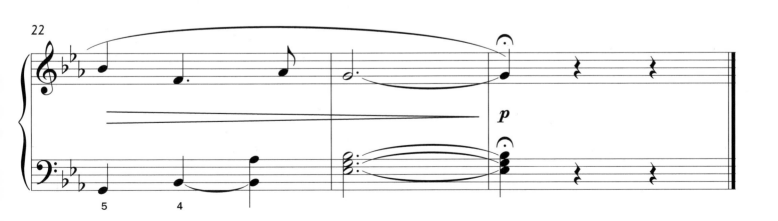

Little Prelude in C

Music by Johann Sebastian Bach

Allegro moderato

Raiders Of The Lost Ark
(Raiders March)

Music by John Williams

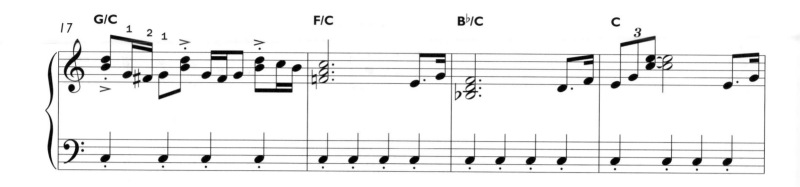

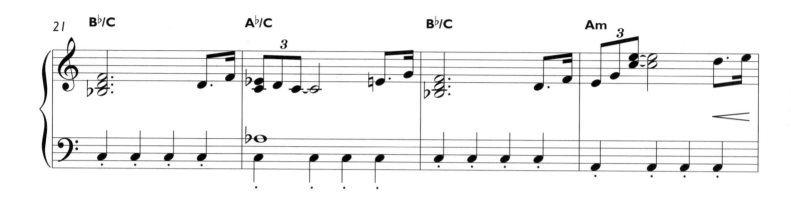

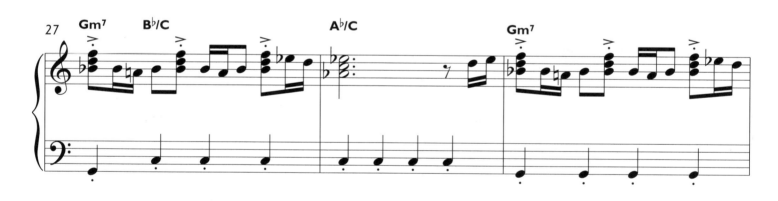

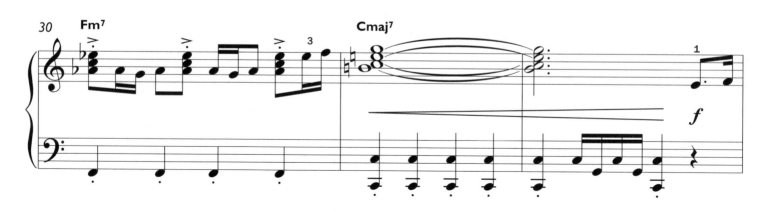

'Moonlight' Sonata

Music by Ludwig van Beethoven

American Beauty
(Any Other Name)

Music by Thomas Newman

Atonement

(Clair de Lune)

Music by Claude Debussy

Andante très expressif

The Godfather
(Speak Softly Love)

Music by Nino Rota

Out Of Africa
(Love Theme)

Music by John Barry

Desafinado
(Slightly Out Of Tune)

Music by Antonio Carlos Jobim

Bossa nova tempo (with a beat)

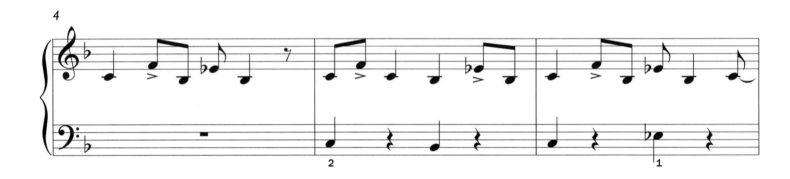

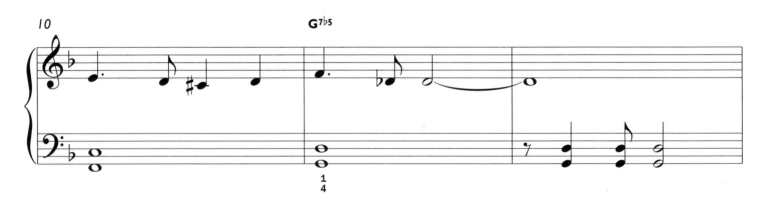

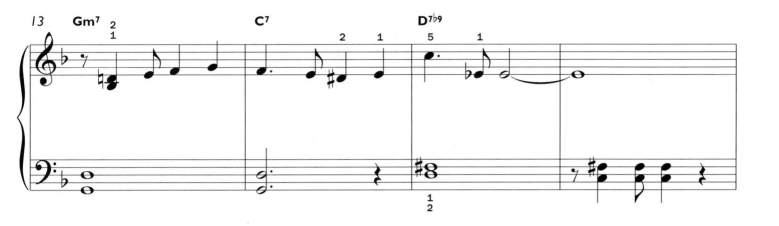

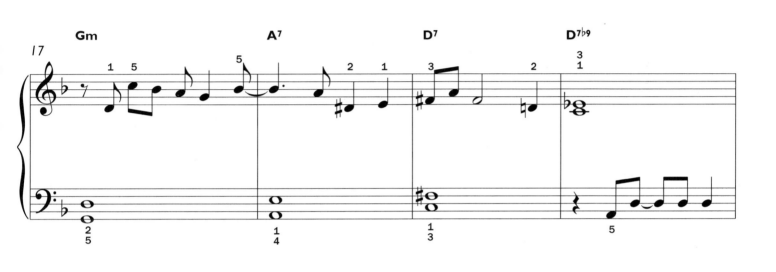

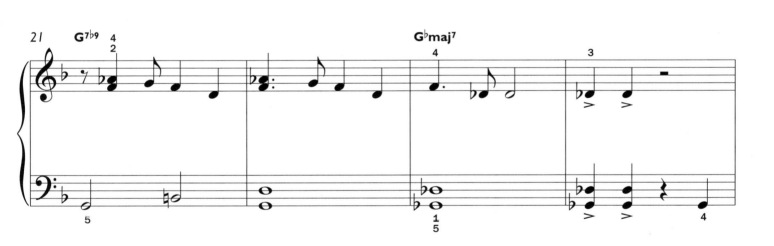

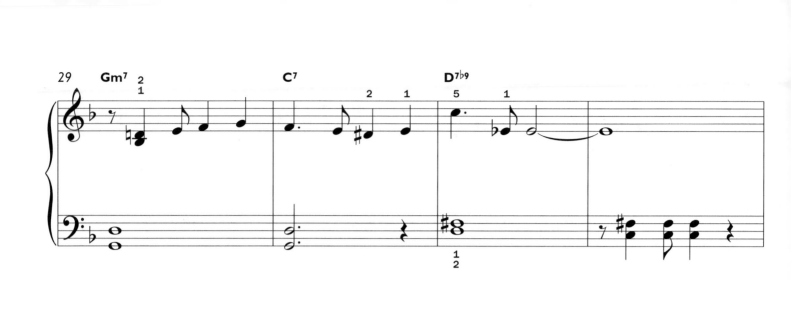

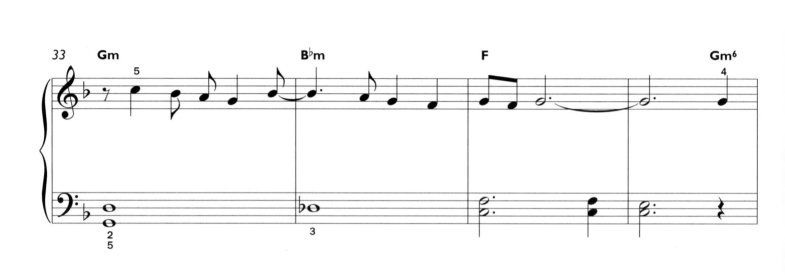

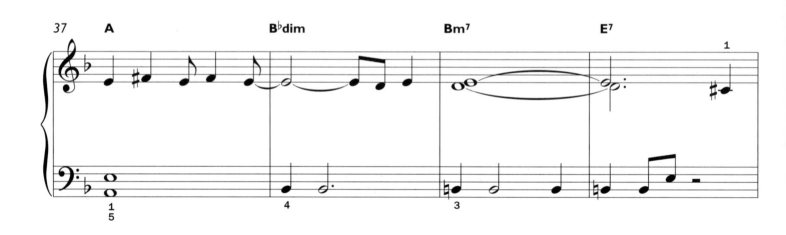

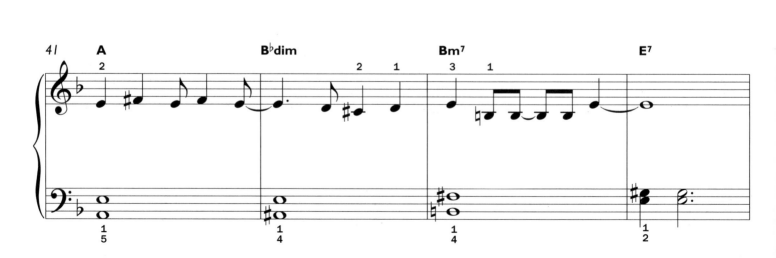

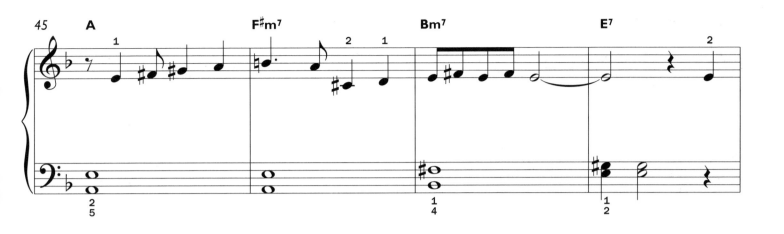

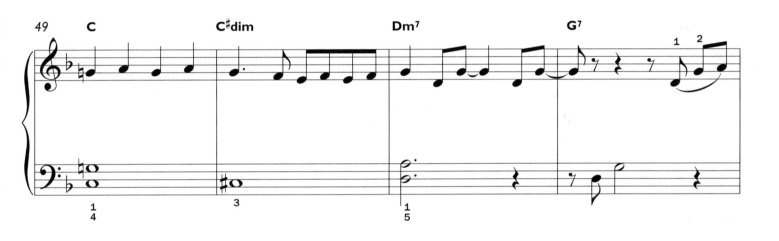

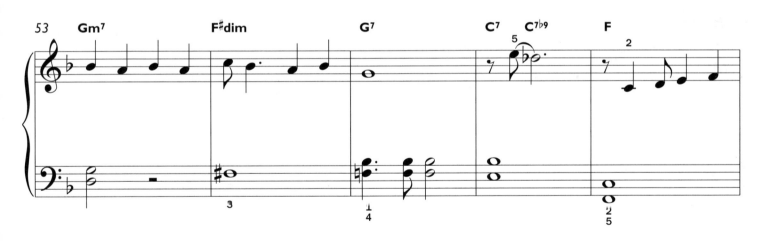

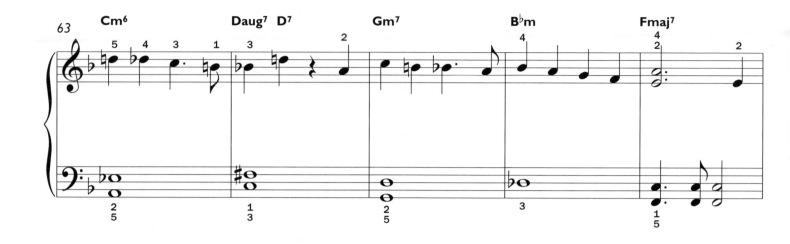

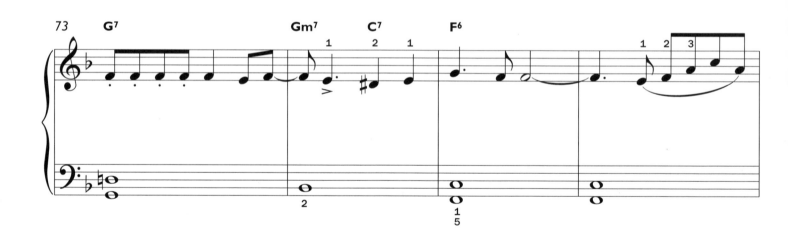

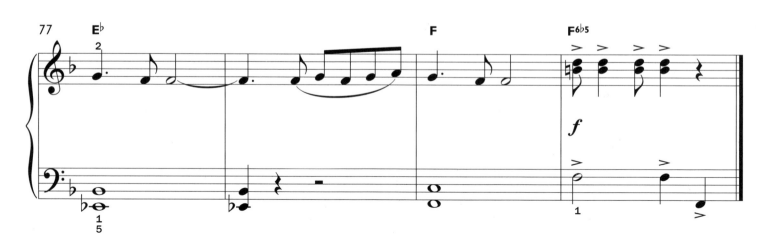

In A Sentimental Mood

Words & Music by Duke Ellington, Irving Mills & Manny Kurtz

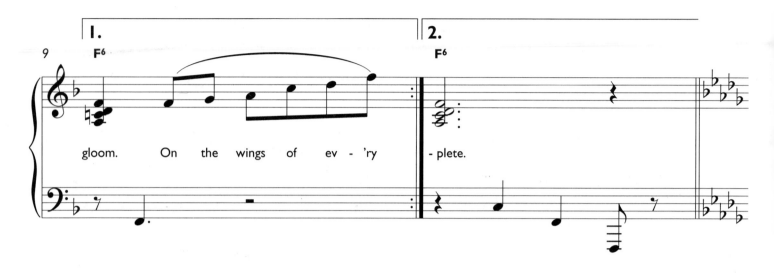

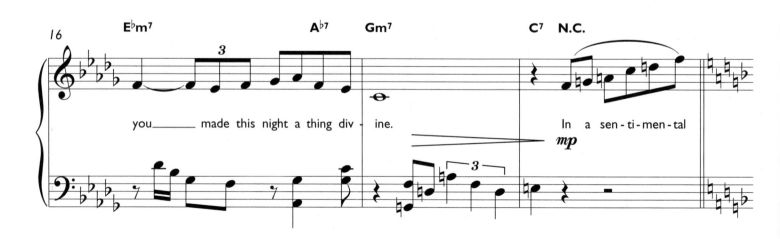

Feeling Good

Words & Music by Leslie Bricusse & Anthony Newley

Fly Me To The Moon
(In Other Words)

Words & Music by Bart Howard

Relaxed, moderate tempo

Fly me to the moon and let me play a-mong the stars,

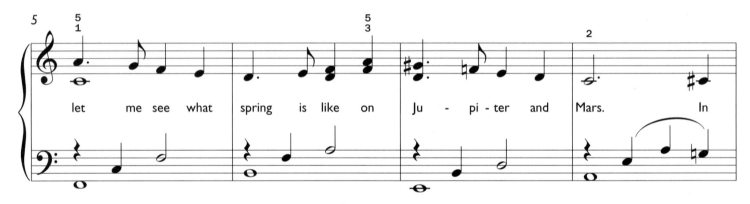

let me see what spring is like on Ju – pi – ter and Mars. In

oth – er words, hold my hand,_____ in oth – er words,

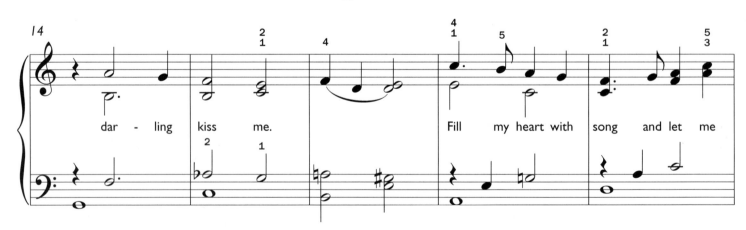

dar – ling kiss me. Fill my heart with song and let me

Smoke Gets In Your Eyes

Words by Otto Harbach
Music by Jerome Kern

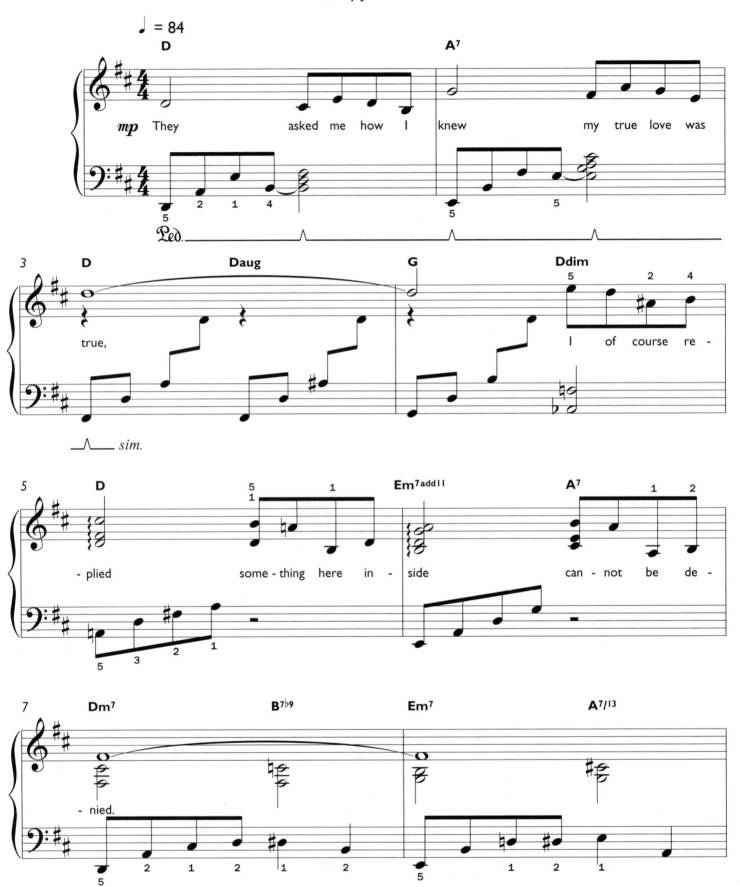

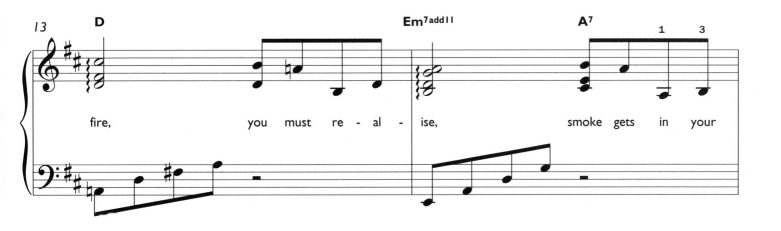

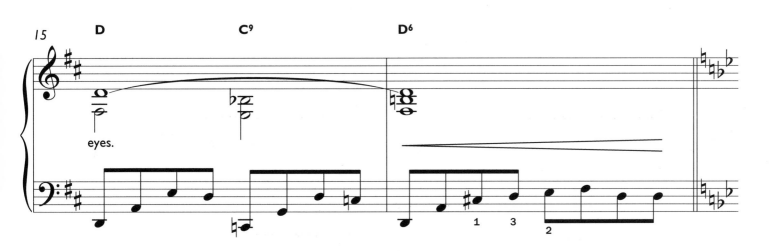

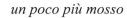

un poco più mosso

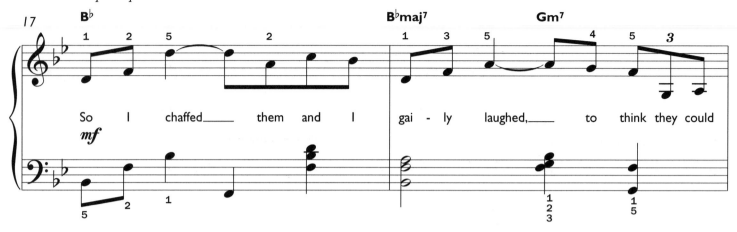

So I chaffed____ them and I gai - ly laughed,____ to think they could

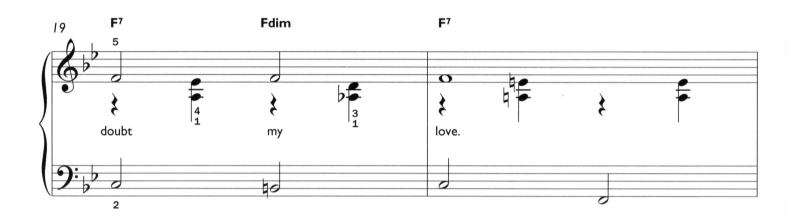

doubt my love.

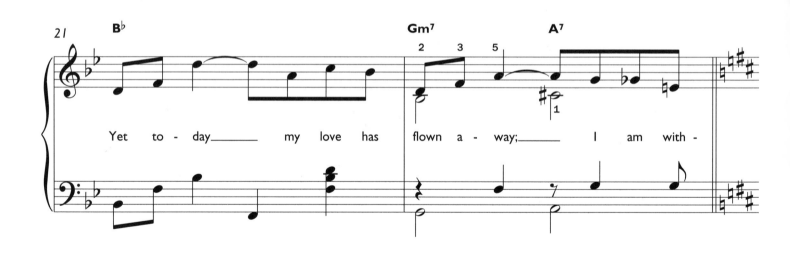

Yet to - day____ my love has flown a - way;____ I am with-

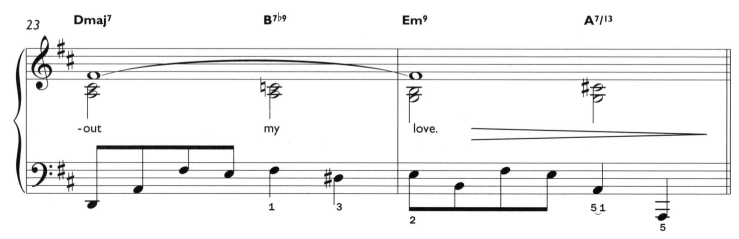

-out my love.

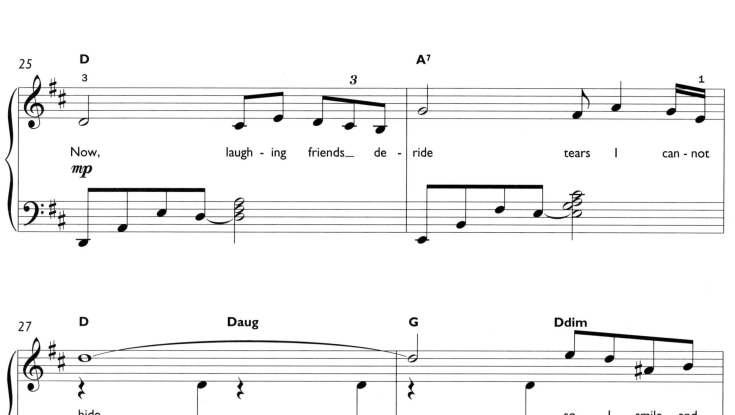

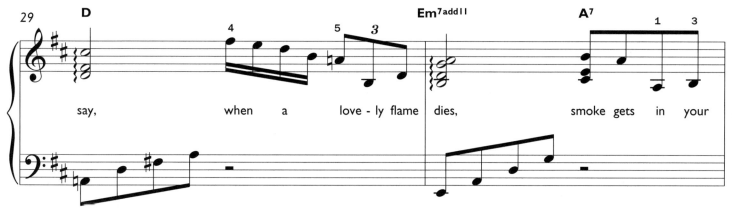

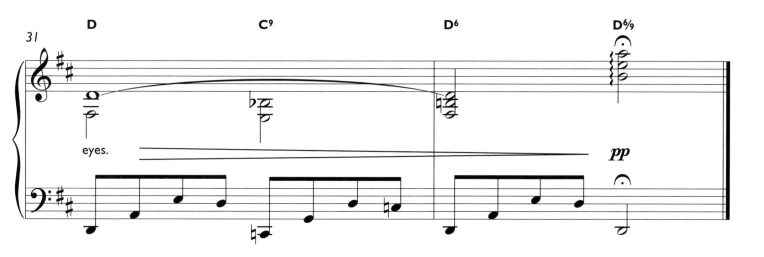

America

Words & Music by Johnny Borrell & Andy Burrows

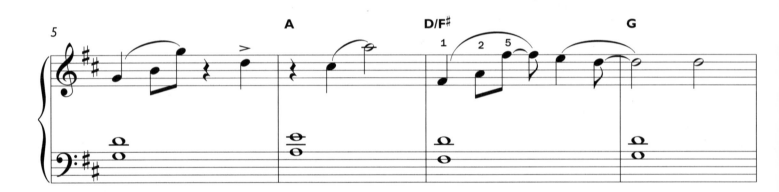

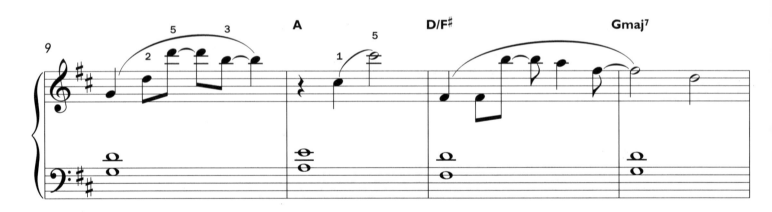

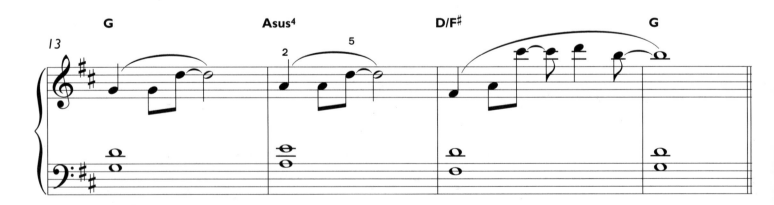

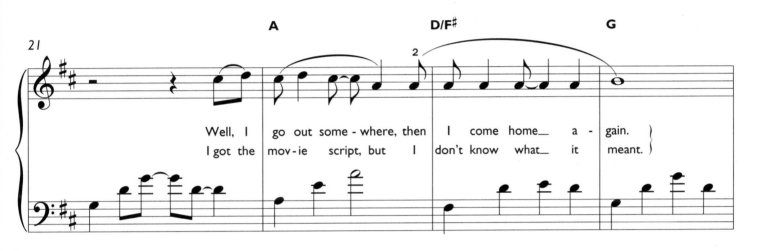

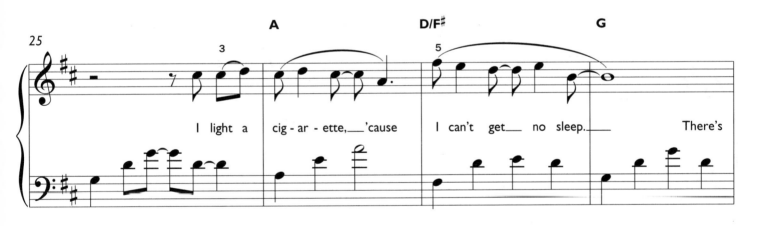

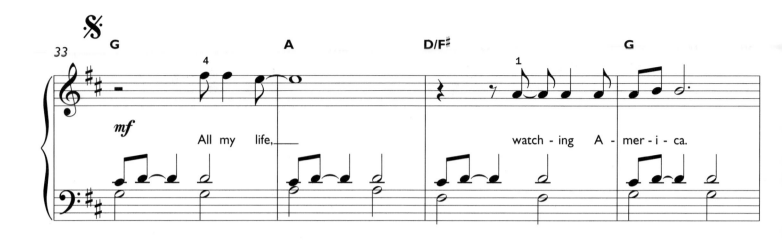

To Coda ⊕

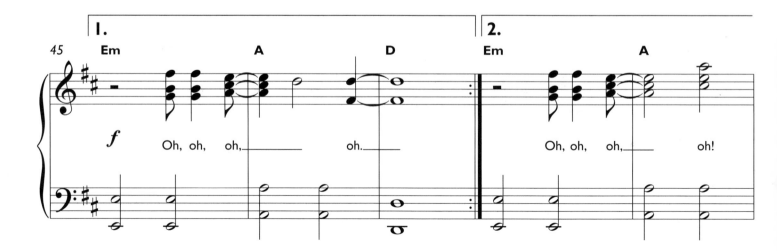

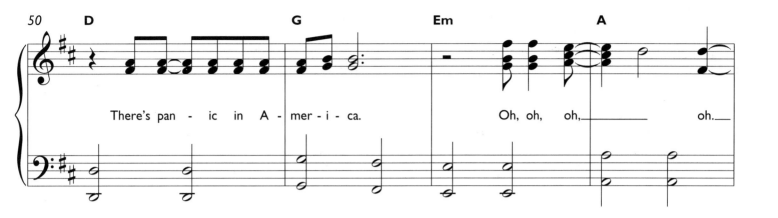

There's pan - ic in A - mer - i - ca. Oh, oh, oh,____ oh.____

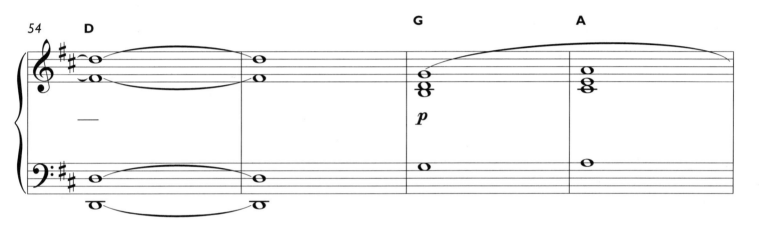

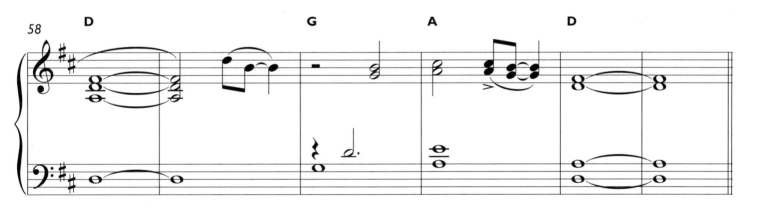

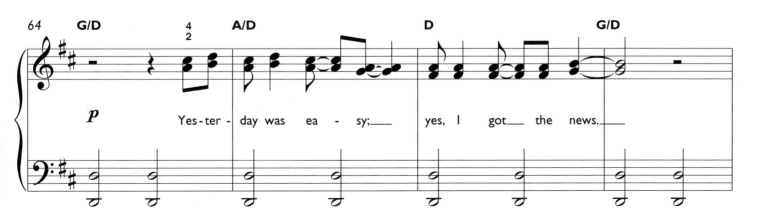

Yes-ter - day was ea - sy;____ yes, I got____ the news.____

Tell me how does it feel?

The Closest Thing To Crazy

Words & Music by Mike Batt

50

51

Beautiful

Words & Music by Linda Perry

Hung Up

Words & Music by Benny Andersson, Bjorn Ulvaeus, Madonna & Stuart Price

♩ = 126

Time goes by so slow-ly. Time goes by so slow-ly.

Time goes by so slow-ly. Time goes by so slow-ly.

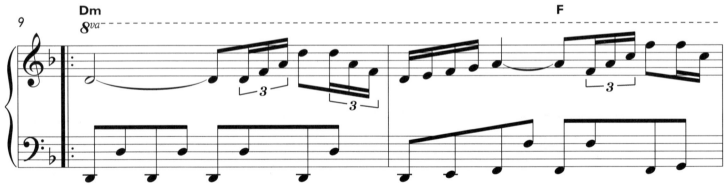

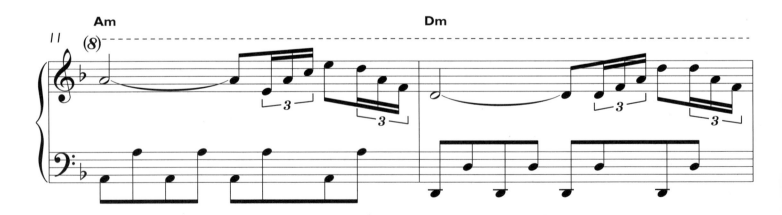

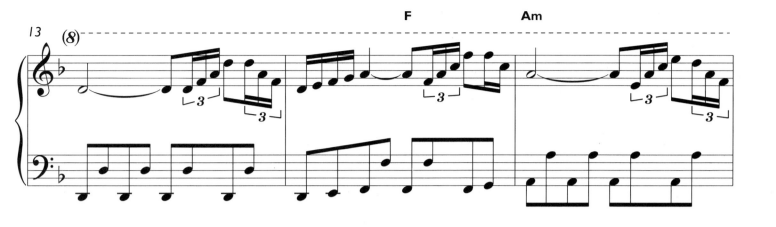

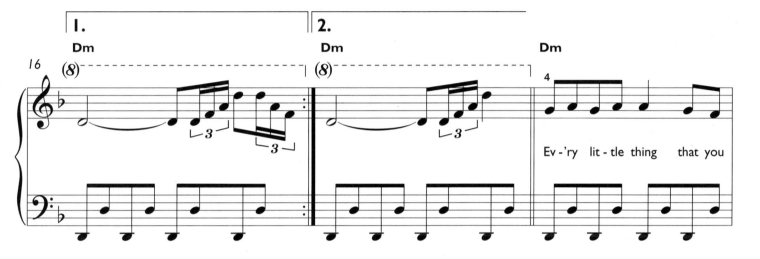

Ev-'ry lit-tle thing that you

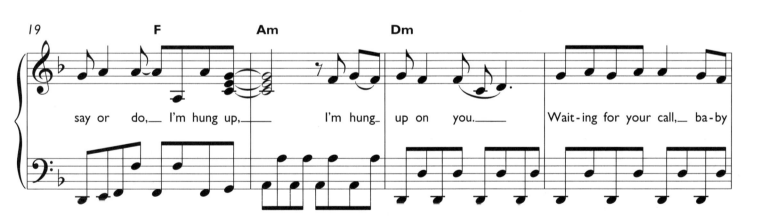

say or do,___ I'm hung up,___ I'm hung_ up on you.___ Wait-ing for your call,___ ba-by

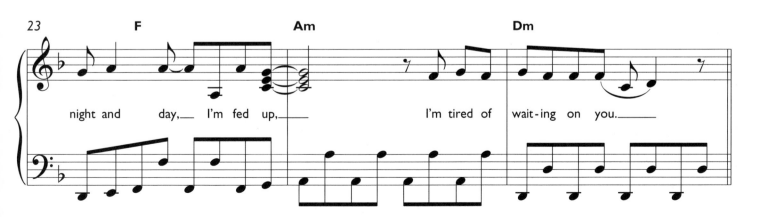

night and day,___ I'm fed up,___ I'm tired of wait-ing on you.___

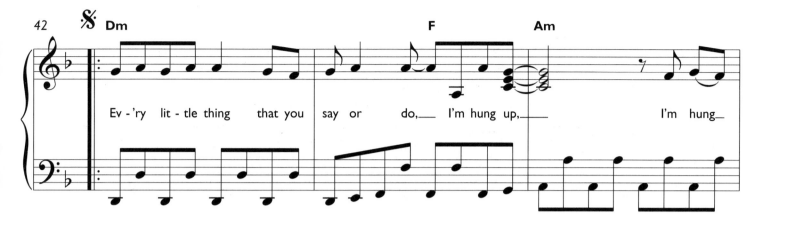

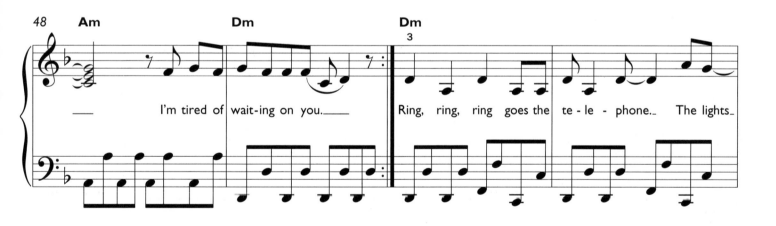

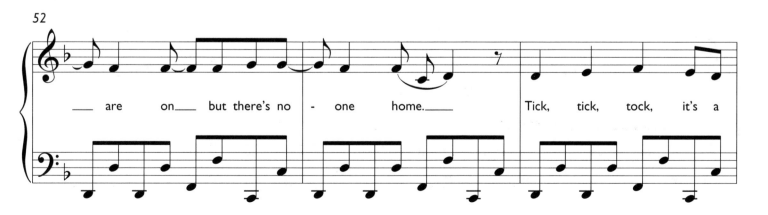

Sail Away

Words & Music by David Gray

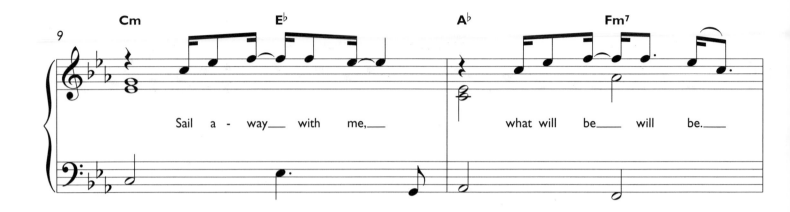

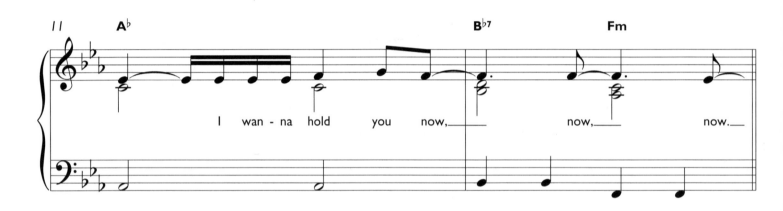

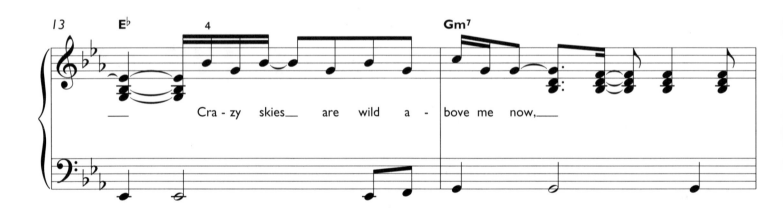

held so dear   dis-ap - peared_ with-out a   trace.__

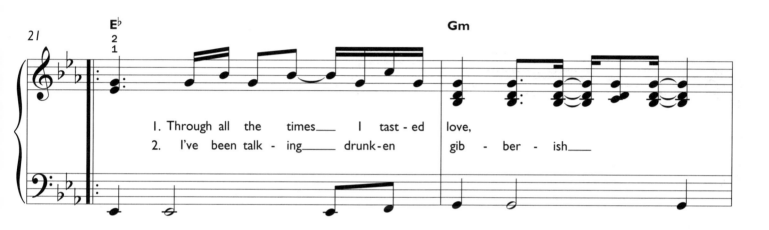

1. Through all the times__ I tast-ed   love,
2. I've been talk - ing____ drunk-en   gib - ber - ish__

nev - er knew quite__ what I   had.__
fall - ing in and__ of   bars.__

Lit - tle darl - ing, if you   hear me now,__
Try'n to get some ex - pla - na - tion here__

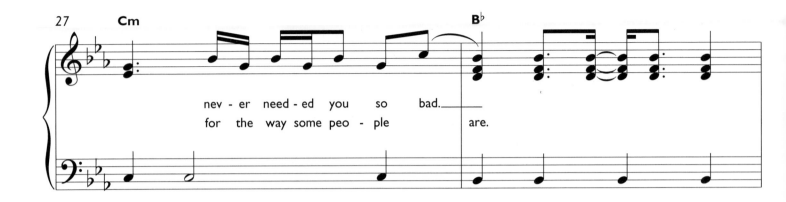

nev - er need - ed you so bad.
for the way some peo - ple are.

1° only

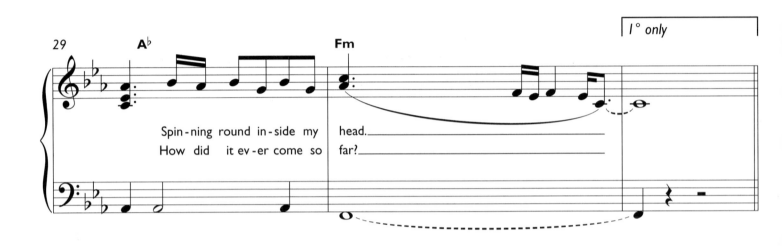

Spin - ning round in - side my head._____
How did it ev - er come so far?_____

Sail a - way_with me ho - ney,   I put my heart_ in your hand.   Sail a - way_with me ho - ney

now,   now,___ now.   Sail a - way_ with me,___   what will be__ will be.___

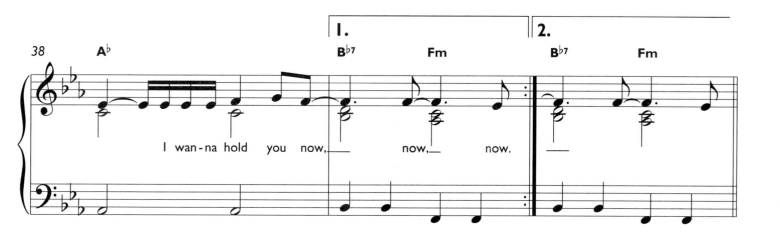

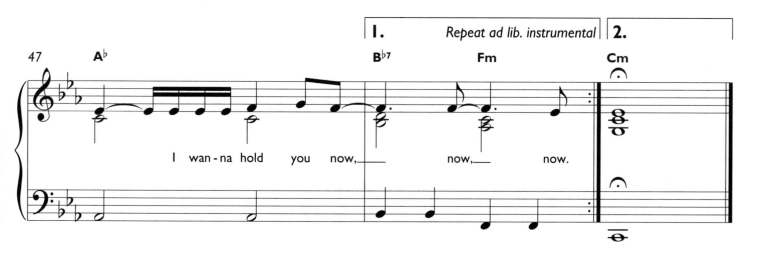

65

Bridge Over Troubled Water

Words & Music by Paul Simon

Moderately, like a spiritual

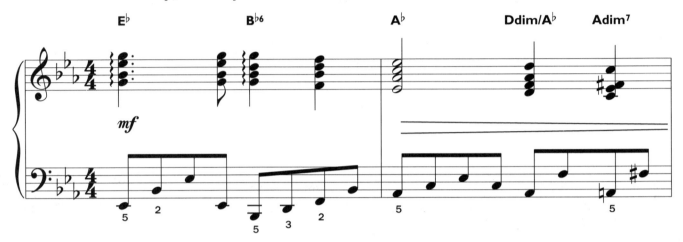

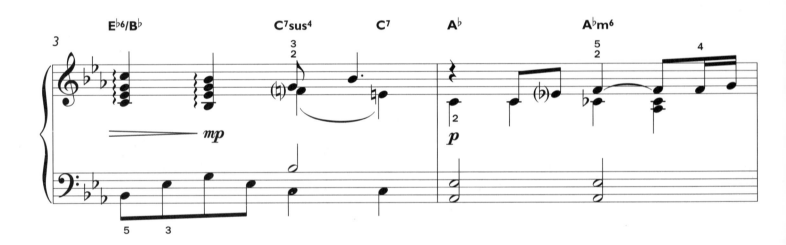

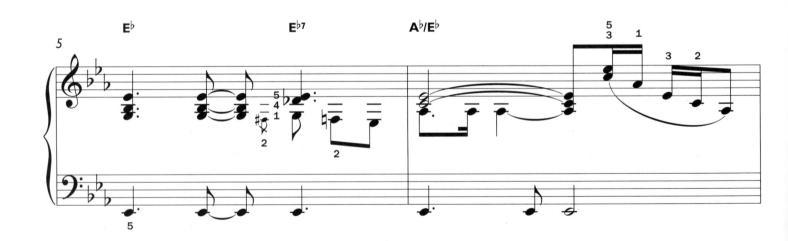

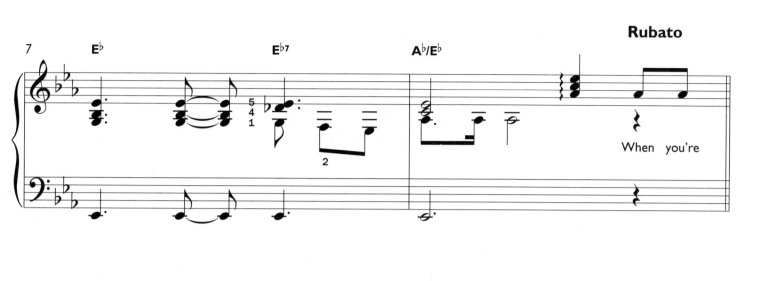

Rubato

When you're

wear - ry,_____
down and out,_____

feel - ing___ small,
when you're on the___ street,

when tears are in
when eve - ning falls

your eyes___
so hard___

I will
I will

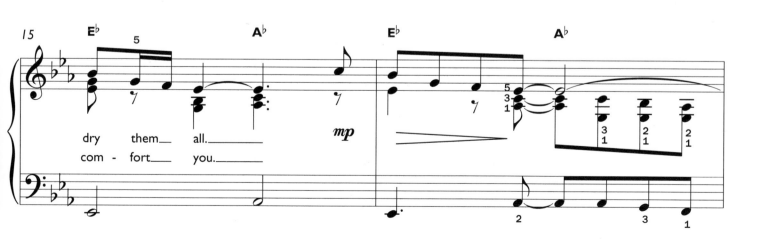

dry them___ all._____
com - fort___ you._____

mp

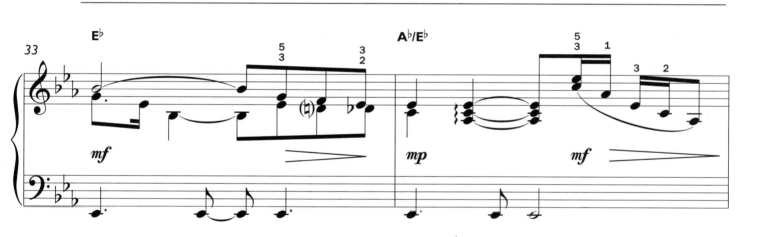

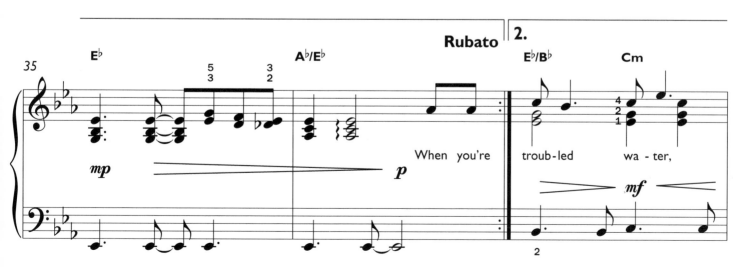

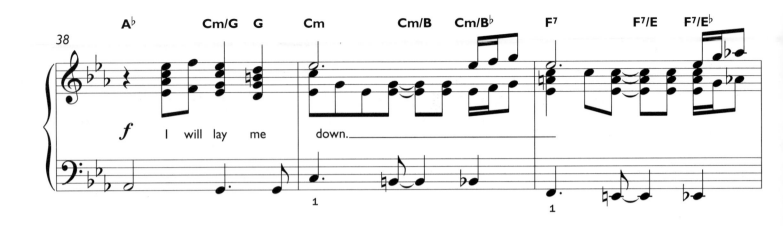

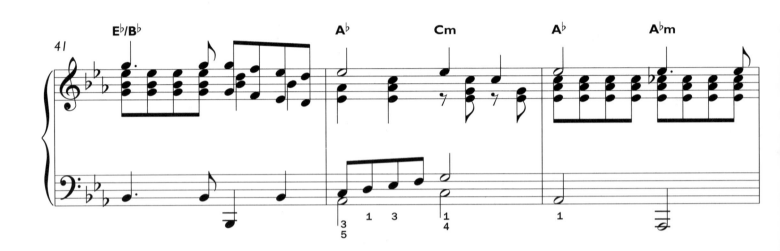

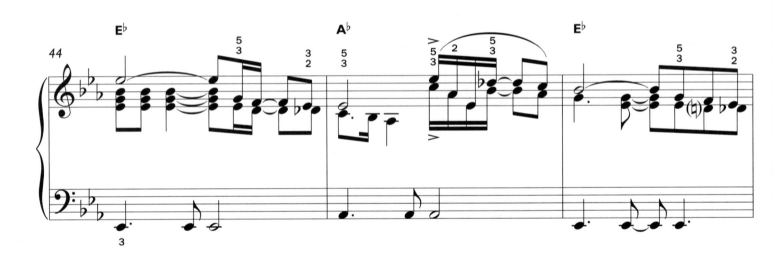

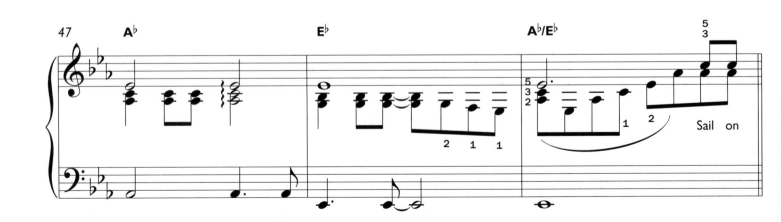

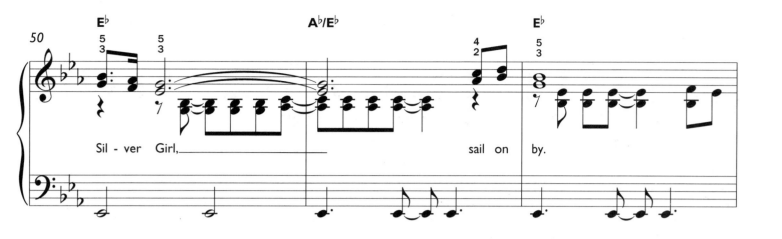

Sil - ver Girl,_____ sail on by.

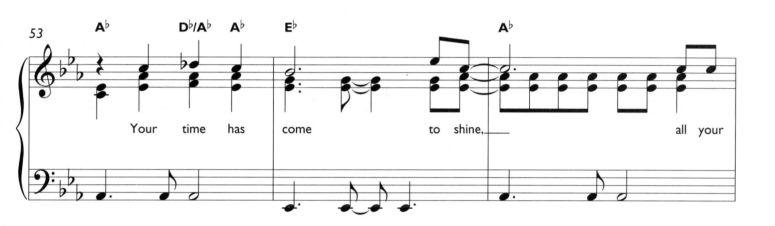

Your time has come to shine,___ all your

dreams are on their_ way.

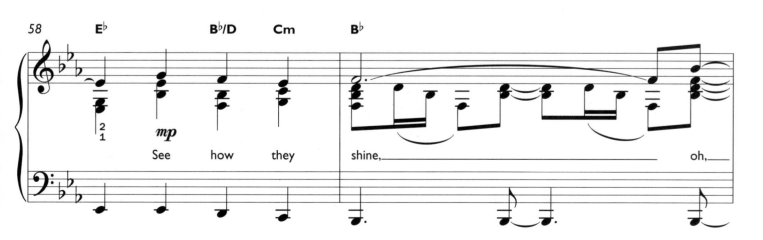

See how they shine,_____ oh,___

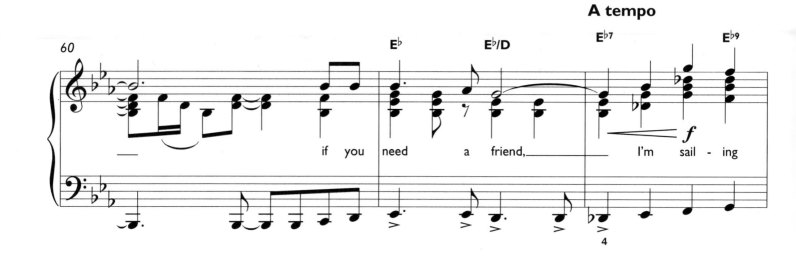

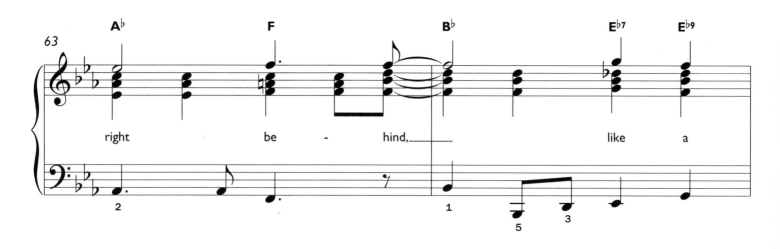

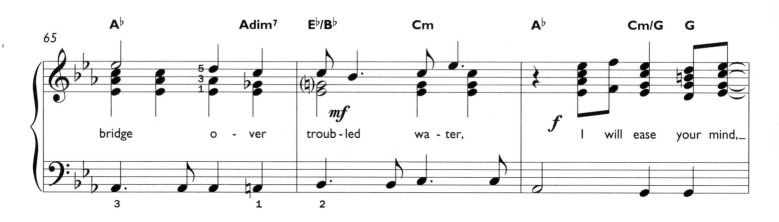

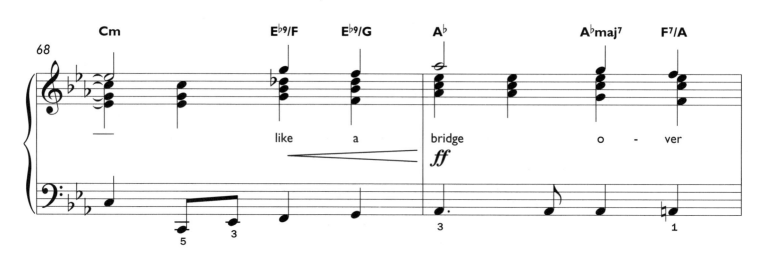

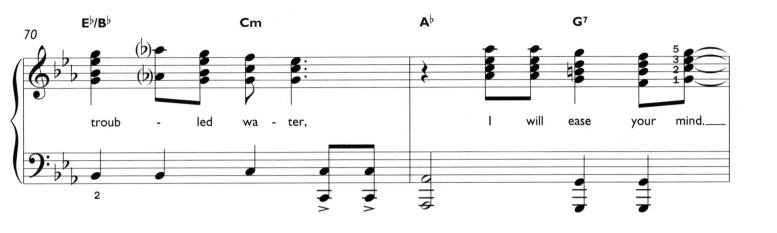

troub - led wa - ter, I will ease your mind.

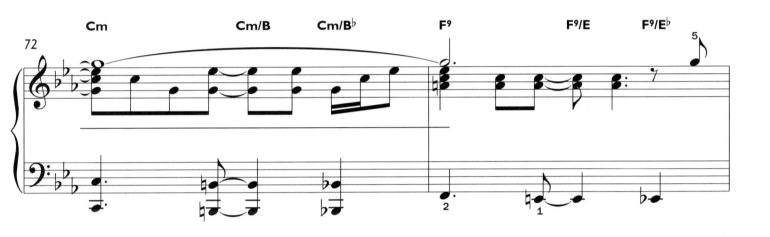

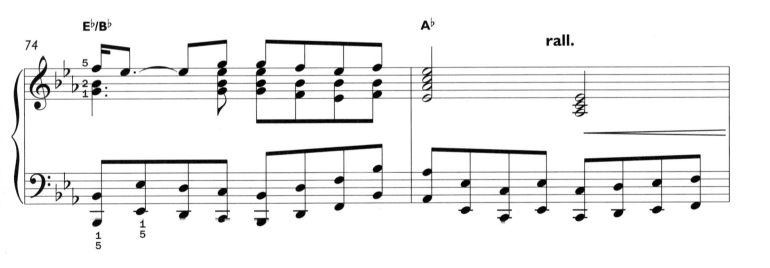

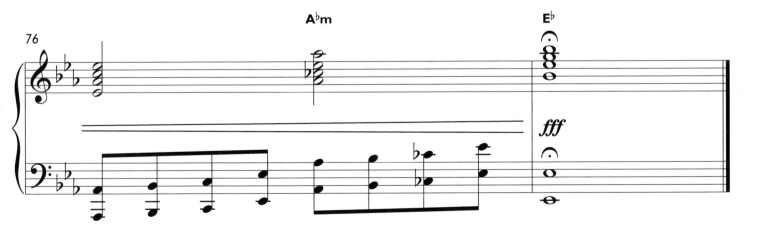

Goodbye Yellow Brick Road

Words & Music by Elton John & Bernie Taupin

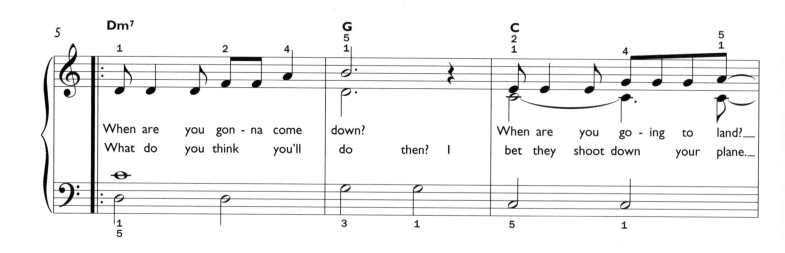

When are   you gon - na come   down?   When are   you   go - ing   to   land?___
What do   you think   you'll   do   then?   I   bet they   shoot down   your   plane.___

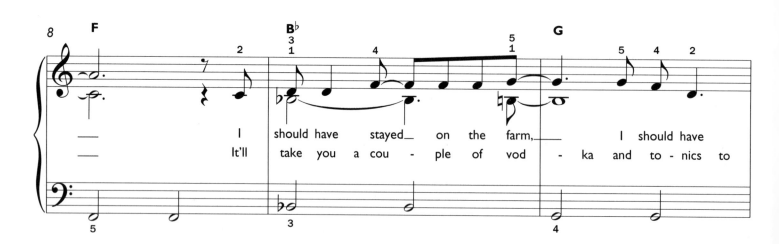

___   I   should have   stayed___   on   the   farm,___   I   should have
___   It'll   take you   a   cou - ple   of   vod   - ka   and   to - nics   to

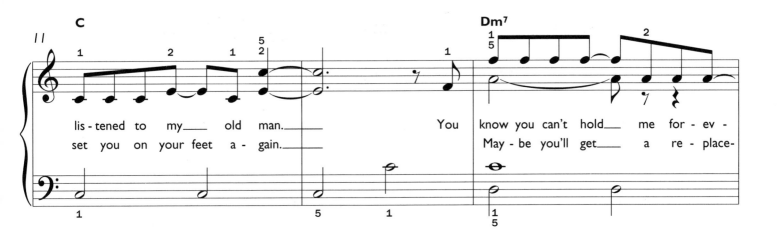

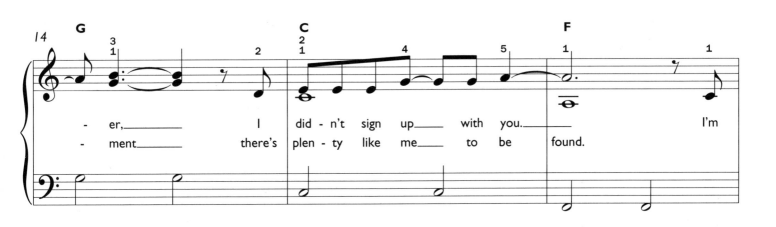

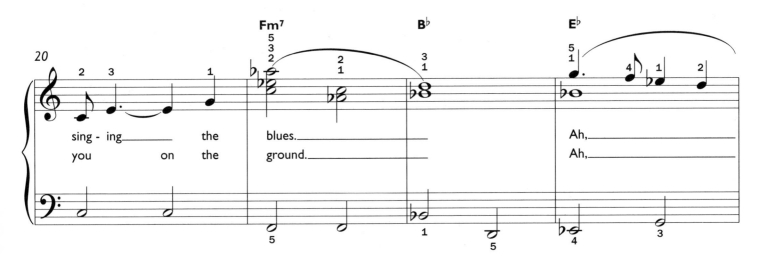

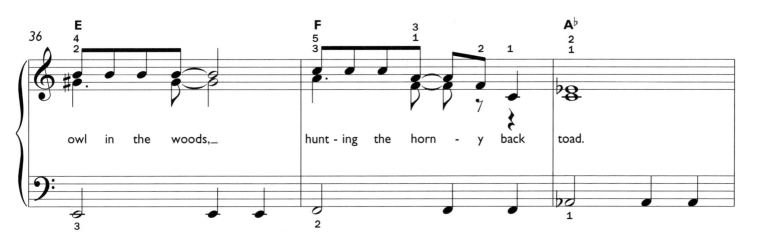

owl in the woods,___ hunt - ing the horn - y back toad.

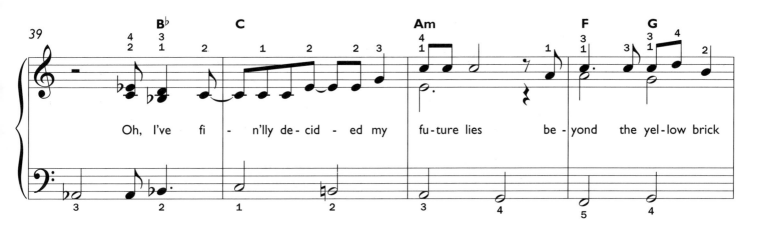

Oh, I've fi - n'lly de - cid - ed my fu - ture lies be - yond the yel - low brick

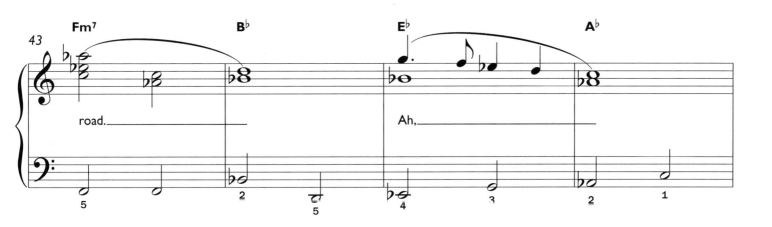

road.___ Ah,___

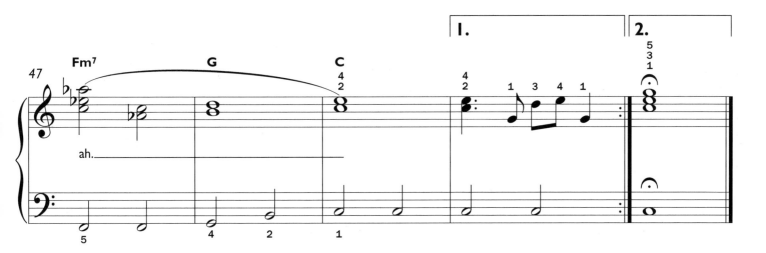

ah.

Purple Rain

Words & Music by Prince

I on-ly want-ed one time too see you laugh-ing._____
Ba-by, I could nev-er steal you from a - no-ther._____

on - ly want-ed to see you laugh-ing in the pur-ple_____
It's such a shame our friend-ship had to_____

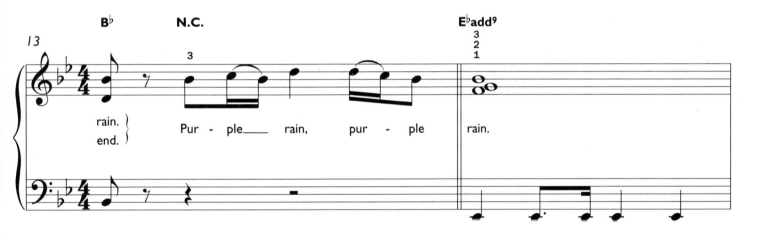

rain.
end.
Pur - ple_____ rain, pur - ple rain.

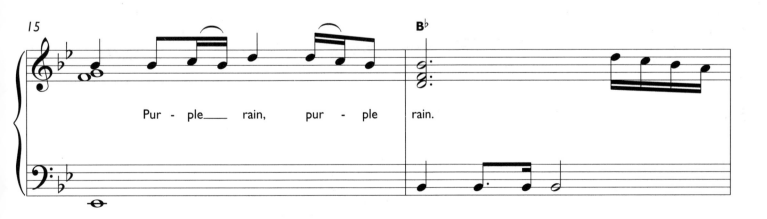

Pur - ple_____ rain, pur - ple rain.

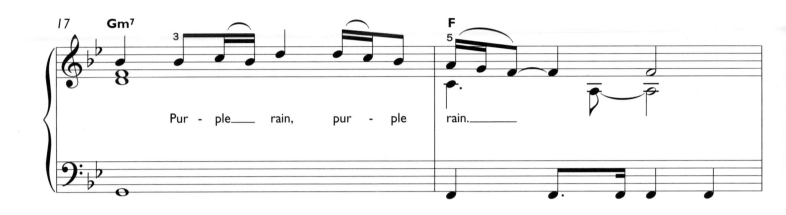

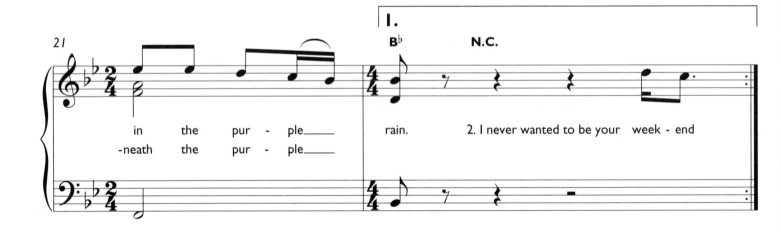

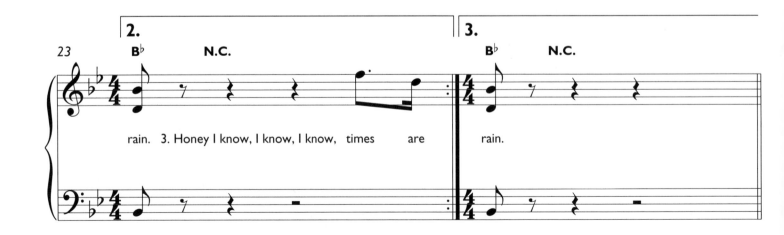

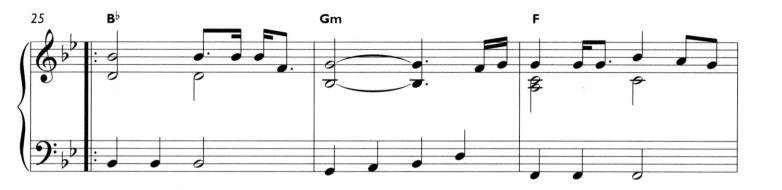

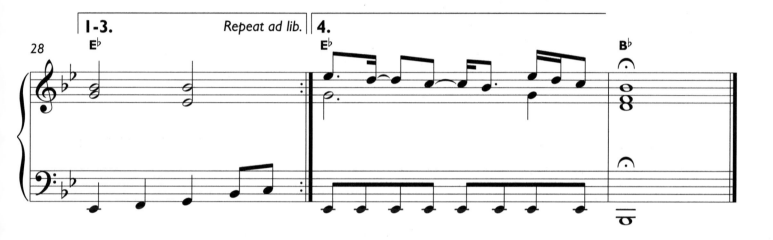

Verse 2:
Honey, I know times are changing
It's time we all reach out for something new
That means you too
You say you want a leader
But you can't seem to make up your mind
I think you'd better close it and let me guide you
To the purple rain.

Purple rain, purple rain
Purple rain, purple rain
Purple rain, purple rain
I only wanna see you in the purple rain.

With A Little Help From My Friends

Words & Music by John Lennon & Paul McCartney

Wonderwall

Words & Music by Noel Gallagher

Today is gon-na be the day that they're gon-na throw it back to you.

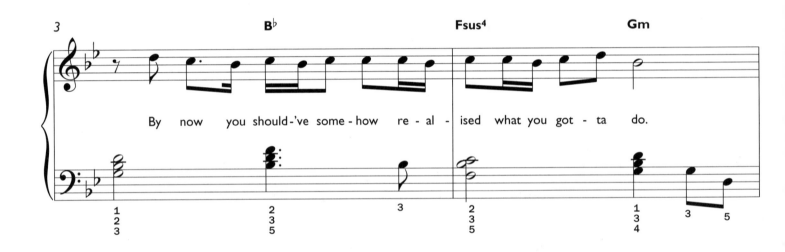

By now you should-'ve some-how re-al - ised what you got - ta do.

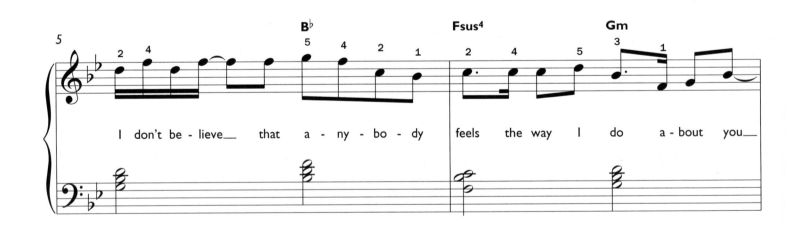

I don't be - lieve___ that a - ny - bo - dy feels the way I do a - bout you___

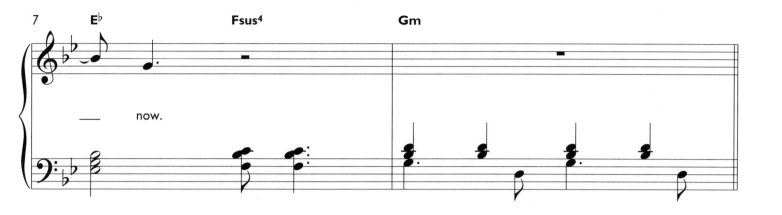

1. Back - beat the word was on the street that the fire___ in your heart is out.
(Verse 2 see block lyric)

I'm sure you've heard it all be - fore but you nev - er real - ly had a doubt.

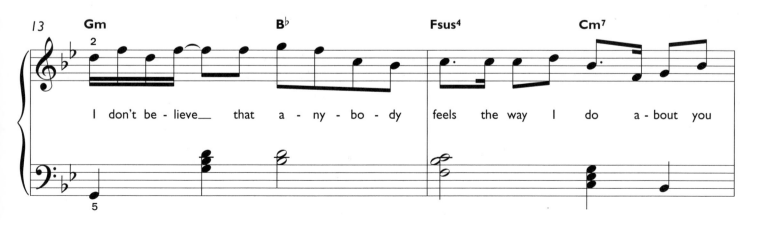

I don't be - lieve___ that a - ny - bo - dy feels the way I do a - bout you

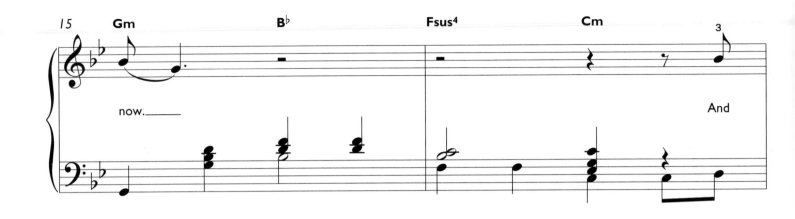

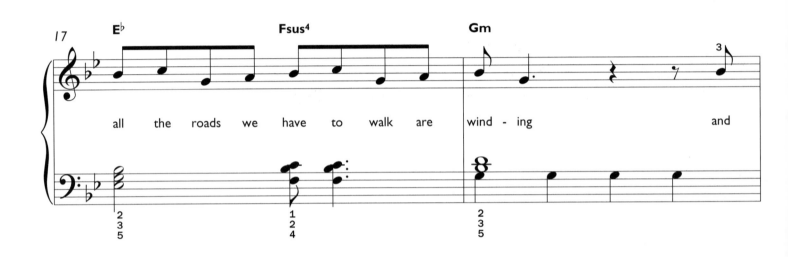

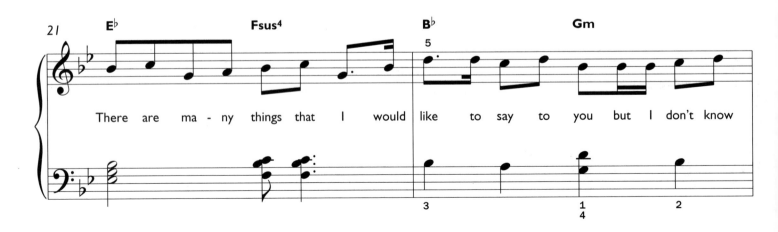

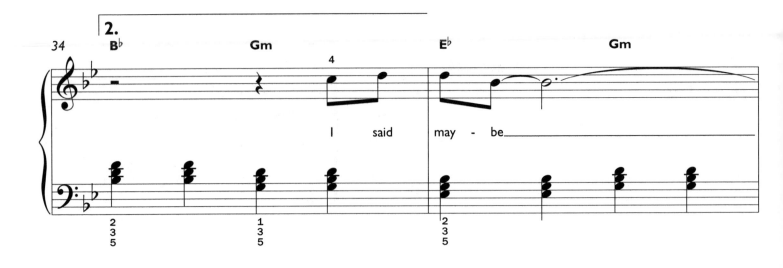

I said may - be_____

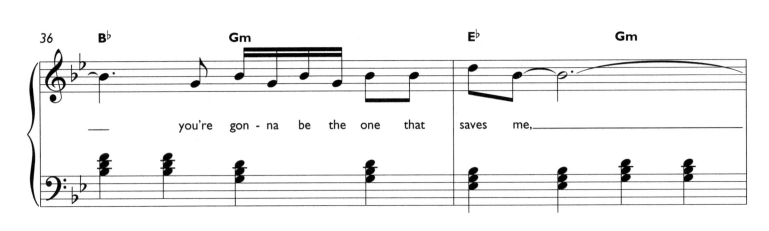

__ you're gon - na be the one that saves me,_____

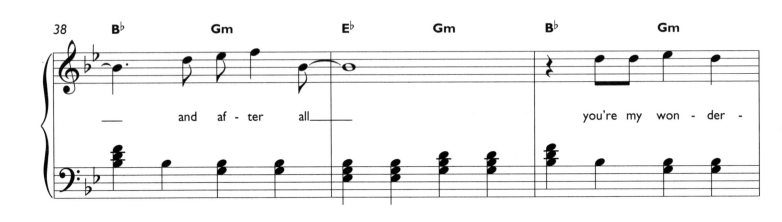

__ and af - ter all____ you're my won - der -

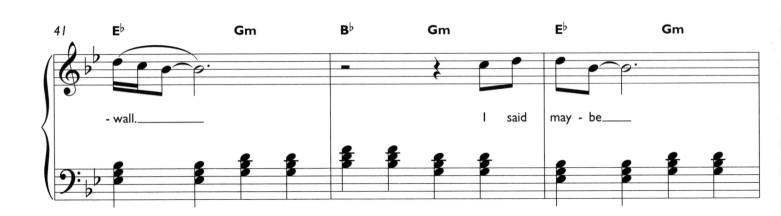

- wall._____ I said may - be____

you're gon-na be the one that saves me,_____

Repeat 7 times

_____ you're gon-na be the one that saves me._____

Verse 2:
Today was gonna be the day
But they'll never throw it back to you
By now you should've somehow
Realised what you're not to do
I don't believe that anybody
Feels the way I do
About you now.

And all the roads that lead you there are winding
And all the lights that light the way are blinding
There are many things that I would like to say to you
But I don't know how.

Big Spender

(from 'Sweet Charity')

Words by Dorothy Fields

Music by Cy Coleman

D.S. al Coda   **Coda**

I Dreamed A Dream
(from 'Les Miserables')

Music by Claude-Michel Schönberg
Original Lyrics by Alain Boublil & Jean-Marc Natel

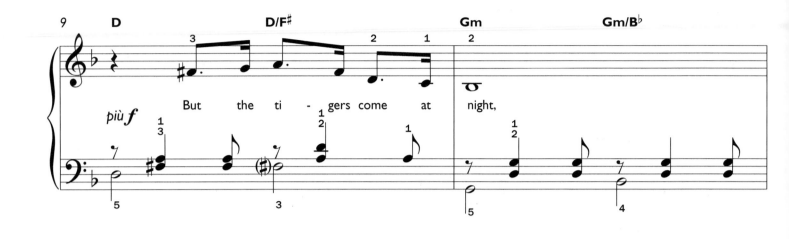

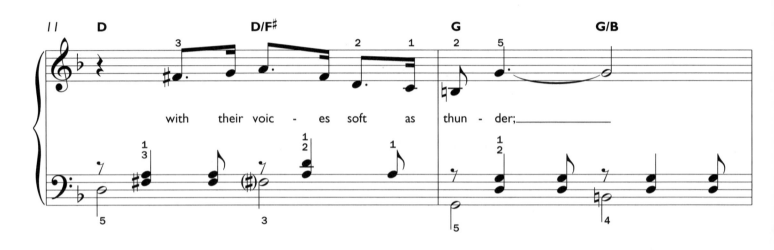

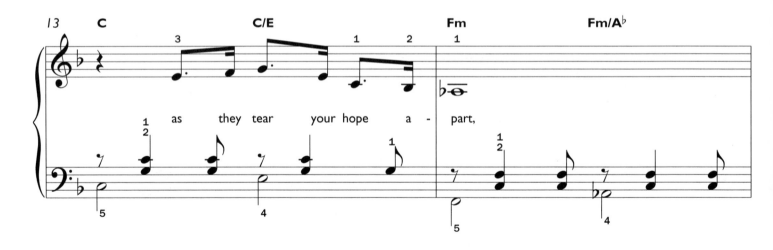

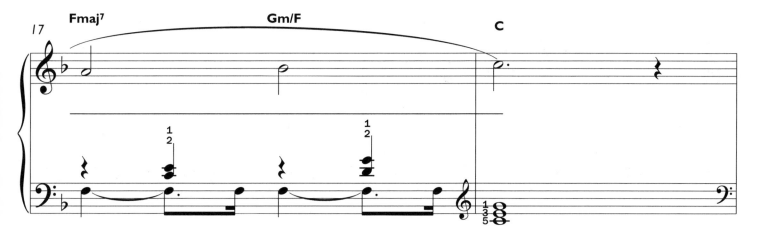

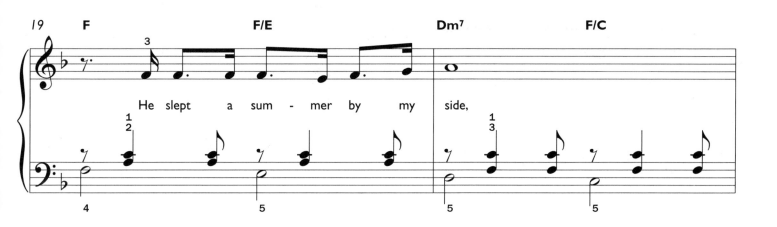

He slept a sum - mer by my side,

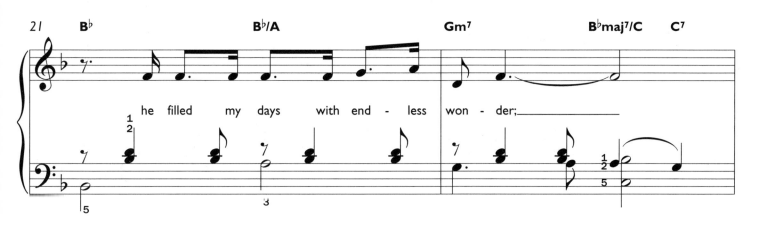

he filled my days with end - less won - der;

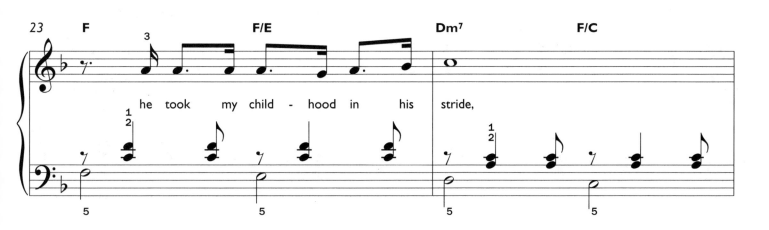

he took my child - hood in his stride,

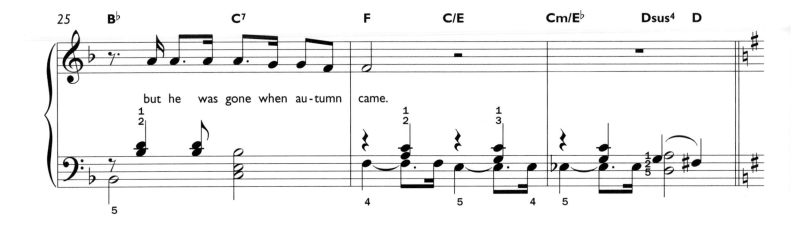

but he was gone when au-tumn came.

And still I dream he'll come to me,

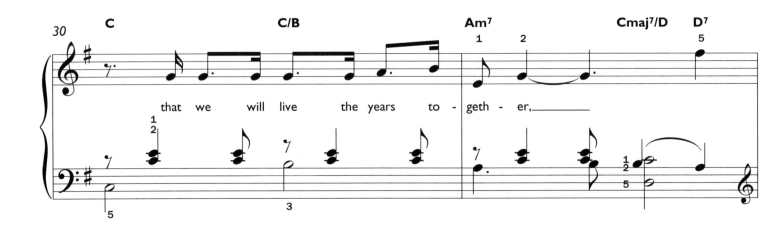

that we will live the years to - geth - er,_____

but there are dreams that can-not be, and there are storms we can-not

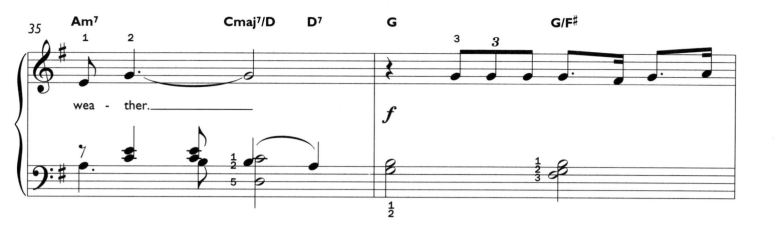

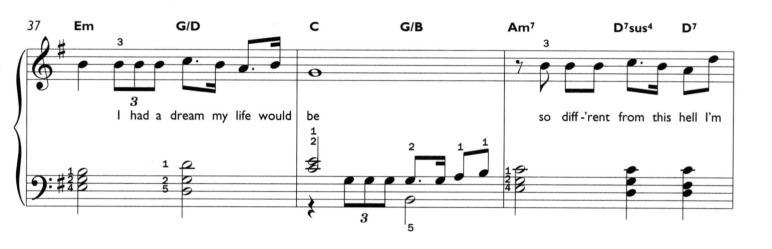

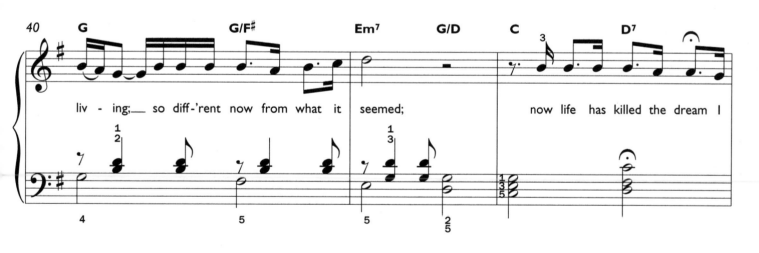

Cabaret

(from 'Cabaret')

Words by Fred Ebb
Music by John Kander

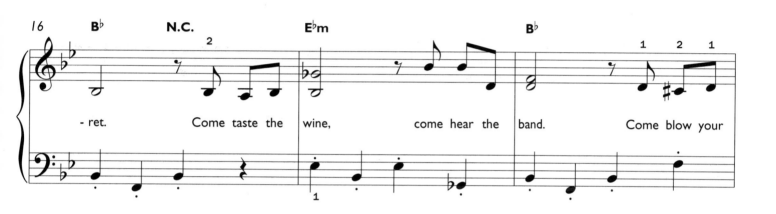

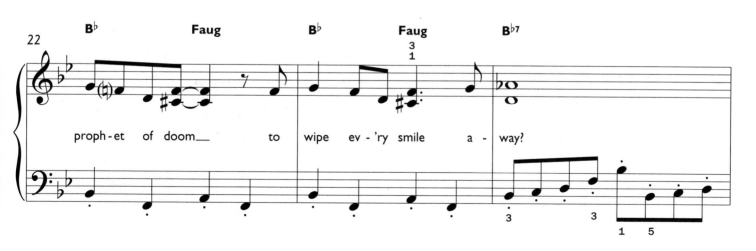

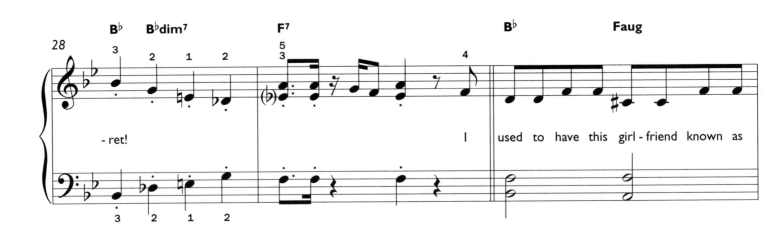

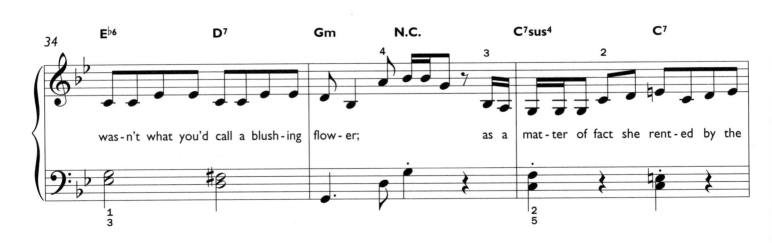

Rubato

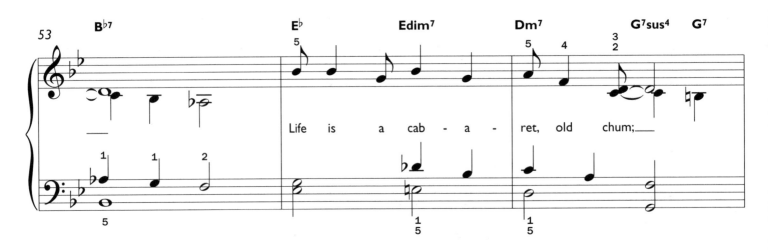

Slowly, with movement   **accel.**   **A tempo**

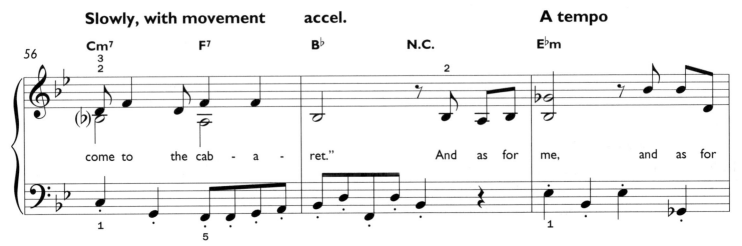

ad lib.

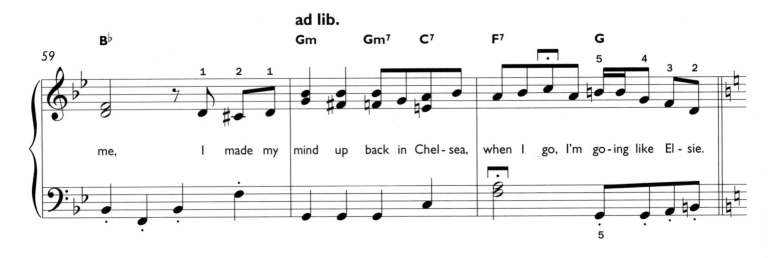

Slowly, accel. poco a poco

A tempo

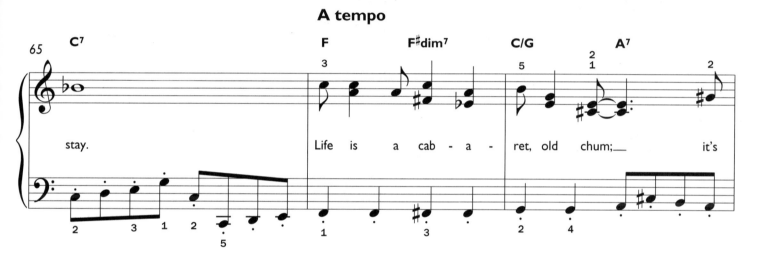

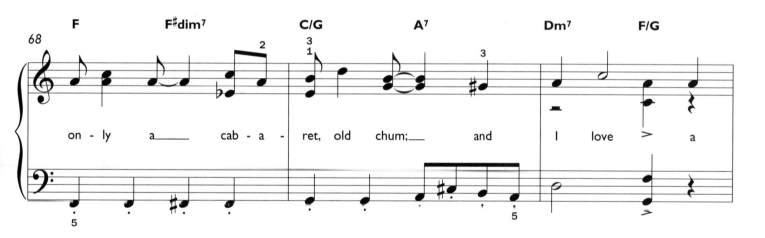

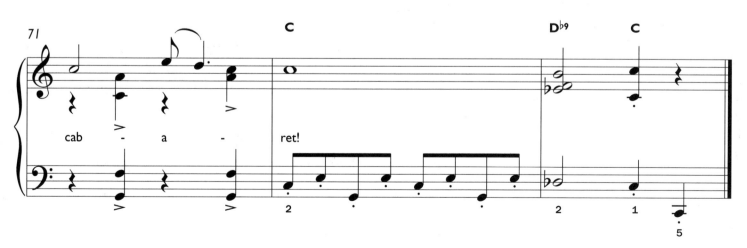

The Music Of The Night
(from 'The Phantom Of The Opera')

Music by Andrew Lloyd Webber
Lyrics by Charles Hart
Additional lyrics by Richard Stilgoe

Andante, with expression

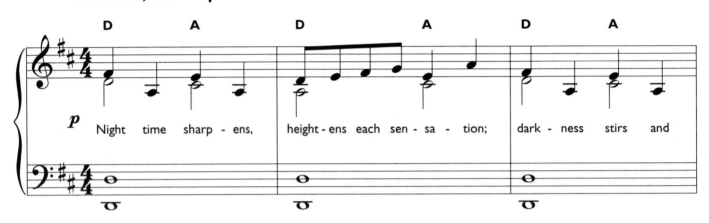

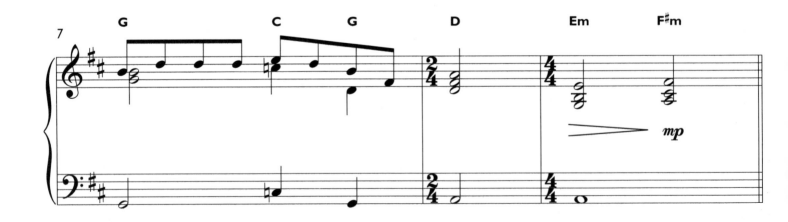

1. Slow - ly, gent - ly, night un - furls its splen - dour, grasp it, sense it,
2. Soft - ly, deft - ly, mus - ic shall car - ess you, feel it, hear it,
(Verse 3 see block lyrics)

trem - u - lous and ten - der. Turn your face a - way from the gar - ish light of day, turn your
se - cret - ly pos - sess you. O - pen up your mind, let your fan - ta - sies un - wind in this

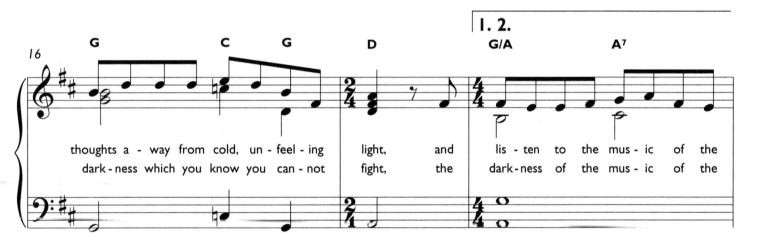

1. 2.

thoughts a - way from cold, un - feel - ing light, and lis - ten to the mus - ic of the
dark - ness which you know you can - not fight, the dark - ness of the mus - ic of the

night. Close your eyes and sur - ren - der to your dark - est dreams, purge your
night. Let your mind start a jour - ney through a strange new world, leave all

thoughts of the life you knew be - fore! Close your eyes, let your spi - rit start to
thoughts of the world you knew be - fore. Let your soul take you where you long to

soar, and you'll live as you've nev - er lived be - fore.
be. On - ly then can you be - long to me.

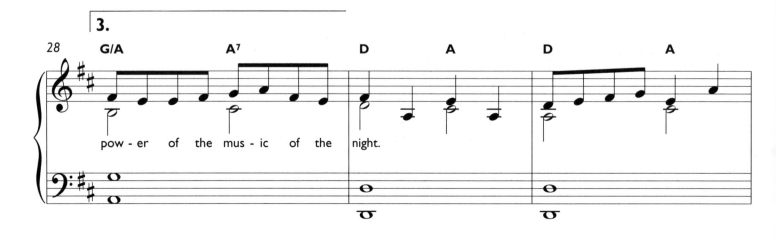

pow - er of the mus - ic of the night.

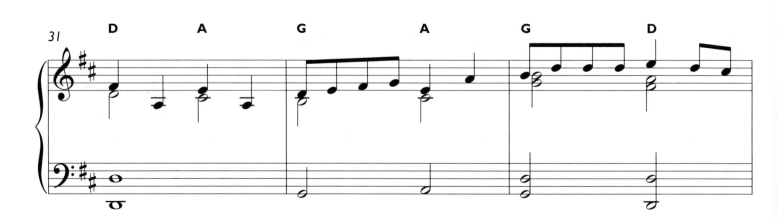

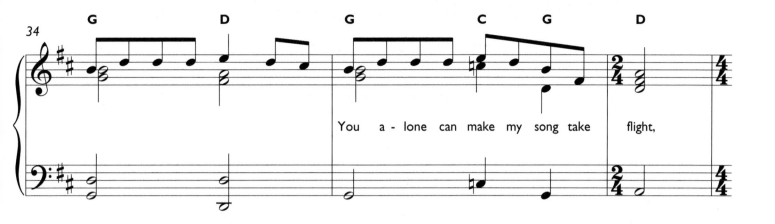

You a - lone can make my song take flight,

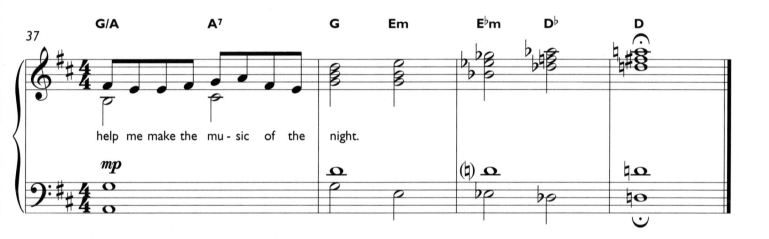

help me make the mu - sic of the night.

Verse 3:
Floating, falling, sweet intoxication;
Touch me, trust me, savour each sensation.
Let the dream begin,
Let your darker side give in to the
Power of the music that I write,
The power of the music of the night.

You're The One That I Want

(from 'Grease')

Words & Music by John Farrar

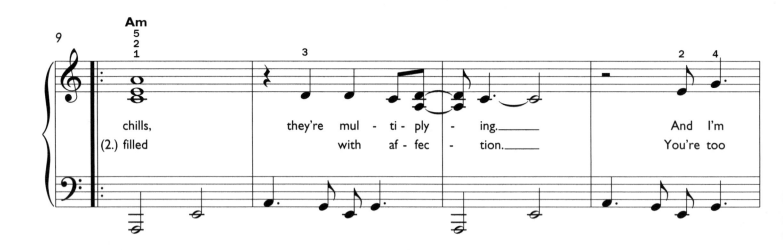

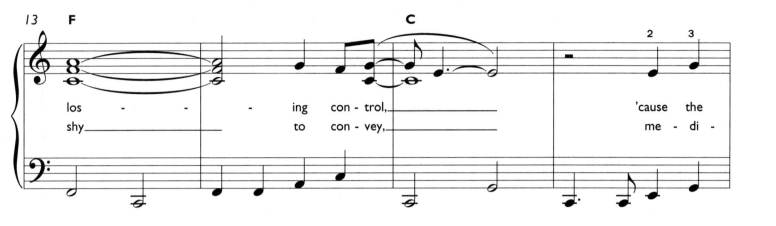

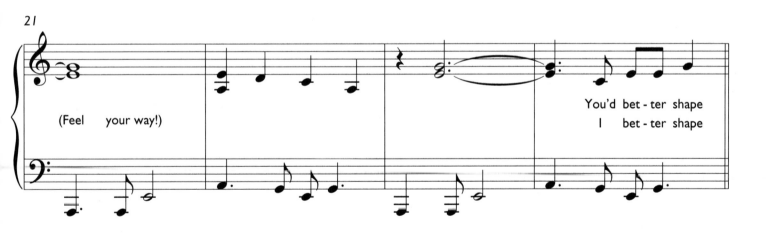

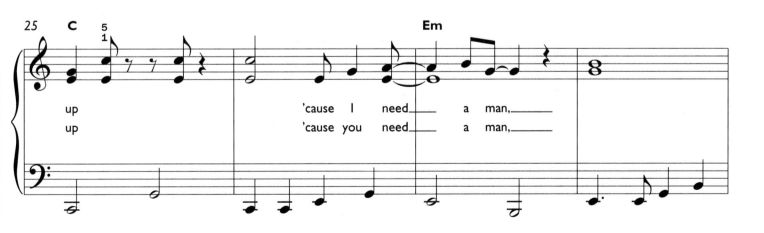

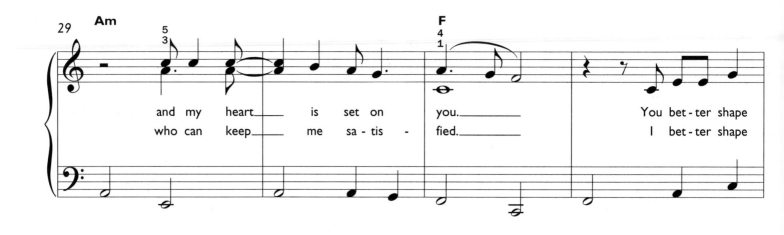

and my heart___ is set on you.___ You bet-ter shape
who can keep___ me sa-tis-fied.___ I bet-ter shape

up,___ you bet-ter un - der-stand___
up___ if I'm gon - na prove___

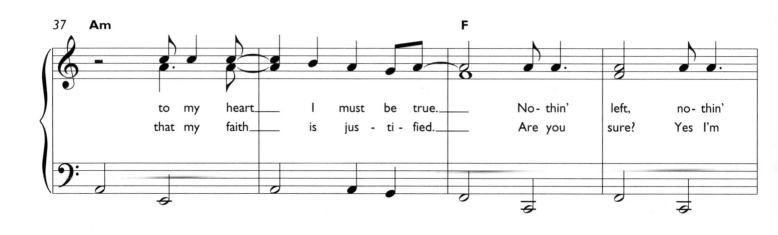

to my heart___ I must be true.___ No-thin' left, no-thin'
that my faith___ is jus - ti - fied.___ Are you sure? Yes I'm

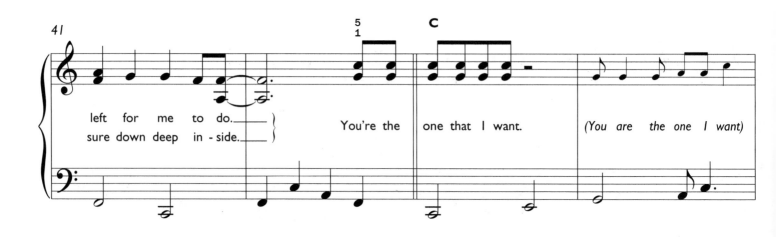

left for me to do.___ You're the one that I want.
sure down deep in - side.___

(You are the one I want)

Ooh, ooh, ooh, hon - ey. The one that I want. *(You are the one I want)*

Ooh, ooh, ooh. hon - ey. The one that I want. *(You are the one I want)*

Ooh, ooh, ooh. The one I need,

1.

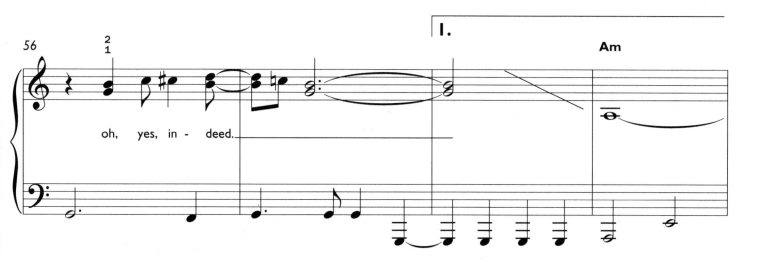

oh, yes, in - deed.

456789
5/11(178404)